# Environment and Health in London

Mark McCarthy

Jake Ferguson

A report to mark the Third European Ministerial Conference on Environment and Health and the Healthy Planet Forum London, June 1999

11-13 Cavendish Square
London W1M 0AN

ISBN 1 85717 274 4

# Contents

**Statistical and health warning**

The data presented come from many sources, and differ in reliability and accuracy. We have used the most recent data available, and where possible for London, but sometimes the only data available are less recent or for larger areas - regional or national.

We have used environmental data as the framework for the report, and linked the health data. This does not imply that the environment causes all the diseases described: but these links are part of the reason for environmental concern. We provide a guide to the strength of the causal links in a table at the end of the report.

THE WORLD HEALTH ORGANISATION European Region Third Ministerial Conference on Environment and Health, and the Healthy Planet Forum, are being held together in London in June 1999.

In a background paper for the Conference, the World Health Organisation says that "Reports on the state of the environment and/or health provide a useful basis for periodic reviews of policy ... The information should be made available to the public in an accessible and user-friendly manner."

This report describes environment and health in London using data that are publicly available.

Concern about the environment is often expressed on health grounds, but the actual connections with health are usually not described. We have drawn on current international scientific knowledge of the links between environment and health. Where there is overlap – for example, several environmental factors can cause cancer – we have used well-recognised health effects. We hope the report will both inform and encourage discussion about environment and health together.

The 33 local authorities in London have legal powers for environmental control, and provide public services. The 16 health authorities (covering between one and four local authorities) control public health and personal health care through the National Health Service. A new Greater London Authority is to be created in 2000. These authorities, government departments, and other national agencies and private organisations are all responsible for environment and health protection in London.

**Mark McCarthy**
**Jake Ferguson**

University College London, June 1999

## Acknowledgments

We are grateful to a wide range of organisations and people in London who have assisted in supplying data in the preparation of this report, and especially Martin Bardsley and David Morgan at the Health of Londoner's Project and Ben Croxford at UCL. We also thank our informal advisory group, representing health authority public health departments and local authority environmental health departments.

Designed by
Susan Rentoul Design Associates
Printed by
Heanorgate Printing Ltd

**London boroughs**

## Key points

London is the capital of the United Kingdom and a major world metropolis. It has a population of 7 million, and is the centre of an economic region (the south-east of England) of approximately 15 million.

- Typically, inner London is worse off than outer London, with higher unemployment, poorer housing, more air pollution and higher death rates. But there is also much variation within each borough.

- Smoking, alcohol, poor nutrition, lack of exercise and excess car use contribute to common diseases including heart disease, stroke, cancer and accidents.

- There are health concerns related to water quality, noise nuisance, refuse disposal and transport of nuclear waste.

- London uses resources equivalent to an area of more than 100 times its size. It will need major economic changes to be environmentally sustainable.

## London needs

★ an action plan for environment and health,

★ better collaboration between public and private organisations

★ good data to demonstrate measurable health improvements

## 1.1a **Where would you prefer to live?**

A national survey asked people to rank where they live in comparison with places elsewhere in England. People in outer London were more frequently positive about their environment than people living in inner London. Both personal circumstances and local characteristics affect the responses.

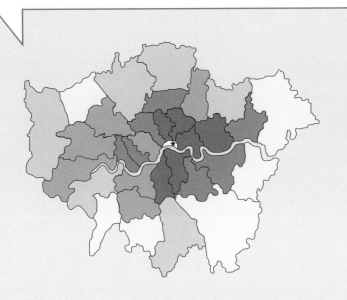

**Index of dissatisfaction**

- ● 15.3 to 17.4 (least liked)
- ● 13.9 to 14.8
- ○ 12.1 to 13.5
- ○ 10.2 to 11.1
- ○ 9.3 to 10.2 (most liked)
- ★ no data

## 1.1b **What do you think affects your health?**

A survey was commissioned by the King's Fund to learn what Londoners believe has the greatest impact on their health. Poor air quality, and too much traffic, top the list, followed by dirty streets. Smoking and lack of exercise are ahead of poor quality local health services.

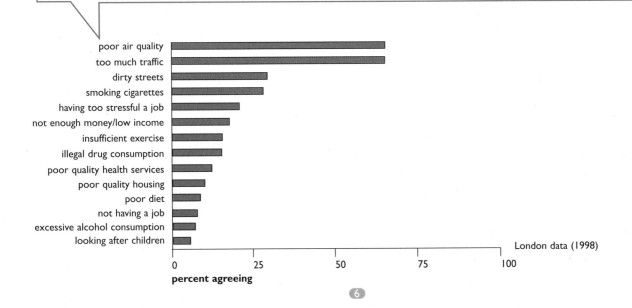

London data (1998)

**percent agreeing**

## 1.2a Population density

London has a population of about 7 million. The inner boroughs have terraced housing built in the nineteenth century and public housing 'estates' built in the twentieth century. Outer London has lower density, typically semi-detached housing, privately owned and with gardens.

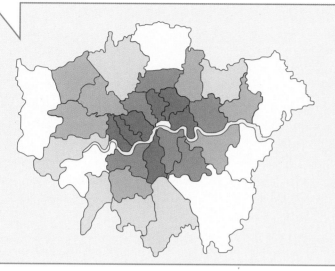

**People per square kilometre (1997)**
- 9,139 to 13,779
- 6,305 to 8,762
- 4,163 to 5,667
- 3,591 to 4,117
- 1,900 to 3,588

environment

health

## 1.2b Going to the doctor

In a national survey, general practitioners keep records of the consultations by patients. Complaints are divided into eighteen categories, some relating to specific diseases (coughs and flu are included in 'respiratory'), while some complaints without a clear cause are included in 'other' and 'symptoms'.

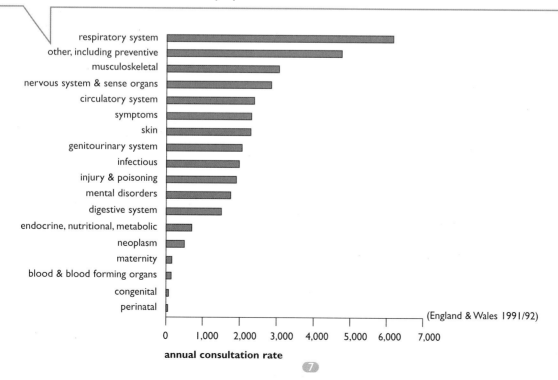

(England & Wales 1991/92)

**annual consultation rate**

## 1.3a **Births**

Boroughs with the highest birth rates form a ring in London where accommodation is less expensive and where there are more families with young children. Outer London has a relatively older population, while central London has more single households and second homes.

**Fertility rate per 1,000 women aged 15-44 (1997)**

- 70 to 89
- 64 to 69
- 61 to 63
- 56 to 60
- 43 to 55

## 1.3b **Deaths**

Inner and east London have higher death rates than elsewhere in the capital. These are also the areas with more unemployment and social deprivation. [Standardised mortality ratios compare death rates adjusted for local population structures. The national average is 100, and boroughs with higher SMRs have higher death rates.]

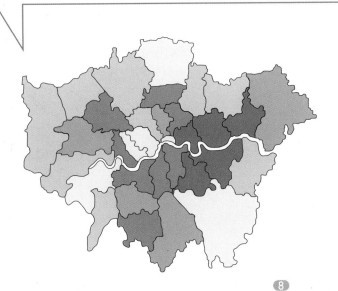

*Data correct according to PHCDS*

**Standardised mortality ratio (1997)**

- 102 to 108
- 94 to 97
- 89 to 93
- 84 to 88
- 59 to 82

environment

health

## 1.4a Migration

London has always been a city of migration. It is the most common place of first residence of migrants from abroad, especially asylum seekers. More than 20% of London's population describe themselves in the census in a category other than 'white'. More than half of national immigration now is by relatives of people already resident.

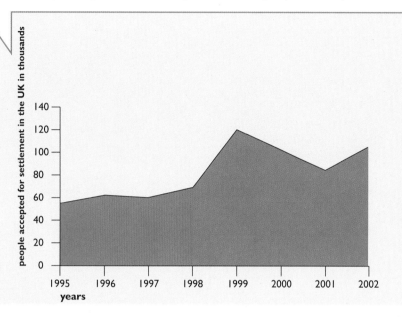

actual
projected

national data

## 1.4b Population change

Population changes by borough are a balance of births and deaths, changes in residence, and migration.

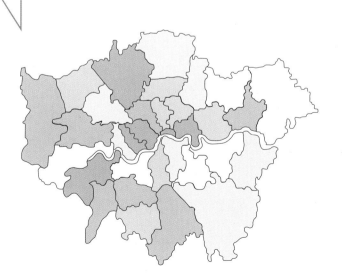

**Population change (1991–1997)**

percent

○ 8.1 to 26.9
○ 4.9 to 6.8
○ 1.9 to 3.3
○ 0.4 to 1.5
○ -1.0 to 0.3

## 1.5a **Employment by sector**

London was once a major manufacturing city. Now services — financial and business, hotels and distribution, health and education — are the main areas of employment.

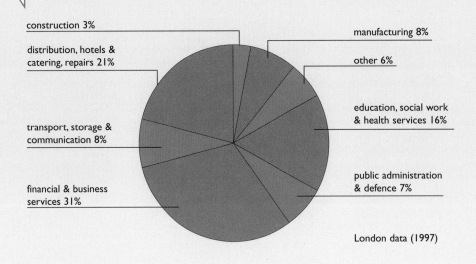

construction 3%

distribution, hotels & catering, repairs 21%

transport, storage & communication 8%

financial & business services 31%

manufacturing 8%

other 6%

education, social work & health services 16%

public administration & defence 7%

London data (1997)

## 1.5b **Unemployment**

The inner London boroughs have higher levels of unemployment than outer boroughs. Yet two thirds of people who work in the City of London — the heart of London's financial services sector — live outside London altogether.

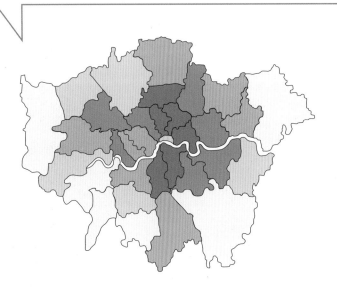

**People claiming unemployment benefit (1999)**

**claimant count per 1,000 residents**

- 49.1 to 64.4
- 33.3 to 45.8
- 22.5 to 28.1
- 16.5 to 19.1
- 11.9 to 15.5

environment

## 2.1a Food safety

Shops and restaurants are inspected by local authority environmental health departments. Businesses across the food trade frequently fail these inspections.

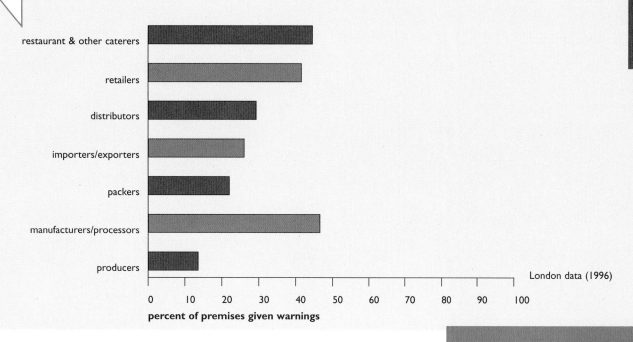

London data (1996)

**percent of premises given warnings**

health

## 2.1b Food poisoning

Food poisoning incidents rose from 4,000 in 1987 to 10,000 in 1997. Food poisoning occurs in both commercial settings and through self-prepared food. Variations between boroughs reflect different standards and traditions for recording, and the number of food handling premises.

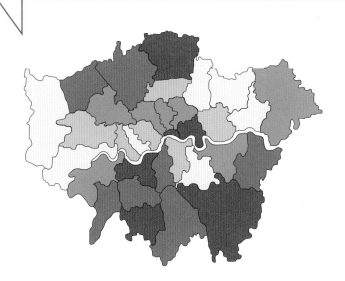

**Food poisoning notifications (1996)**

rate per 100,000

- 183 to 479
- 149 to 176
- 108 to 142
- 70 to 97
- 21 to 69

## 2.2a Food consumption

London is showing beneficial trends in food consumption patterns from a health perspective – less fat, less meat, more fruit and more bread, although a fall in consumption of vegetables is unwelcome.

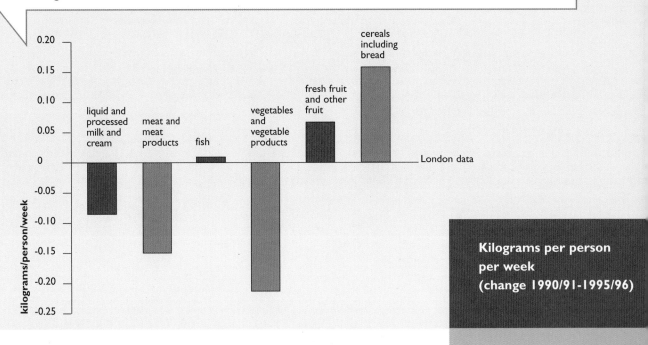

**Kilograms per person per week (change 1990/91-1995/96)**

## 2.2b Obesity

Poor diet and lack of exercise are contributing to rising obesity in Londoners.

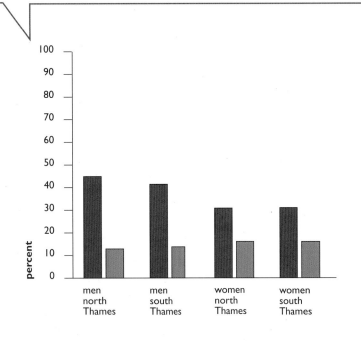

■ obese BMI over 30
■ overweight BMI over 25

**BMI= Body Mass Index**

Regional data (1996)

environment

health

environment

health

## 2.3a **Premises licensed for alcohol**

Selling alcohol in a shop, pub or restaurant requires a license from a magistrate. Some boroughs have more than 1,000 places licensed to sell alcohol.

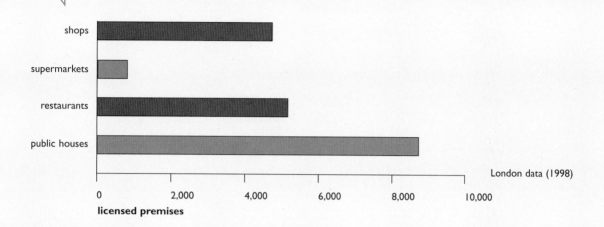

London data (1998)

**licensed premises**

## 2.3b **Cirrhosis**

Excess alcohol consumption contributes to many health risks, including accidents, suicide, neurological diseases and liver cirrhosis.

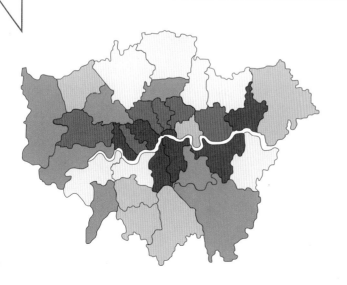

**Chronic liver disease deaths (1997)**

rate per 100,000

- 13.8 to 23.6
- 11.9 to 13.5
- 8.6 to 11.8
- 7.6 to  8.0
- 4.1 to  7.1

## 2.4a Smoking

London smokers average 10 -15 cigarettes a day. One in two smokers who started in their youth and continue smoking will die from tobacco-related disease. Although fewer men are smoking than previously, there has been a rising proportion of women smoking.

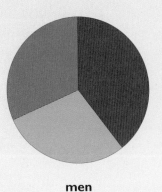

**men**

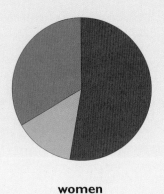

**women**

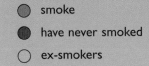

- ⬤ smoke
- ⬤ have never smoked
- ◯ ex-smokers

London data (1996/97)

## 2.4b Lung cancer

Most lung cancer is caused by cigarette smoking. Lung cancer is not easily treated, and patients rarely survive up to five years from diagnosis.

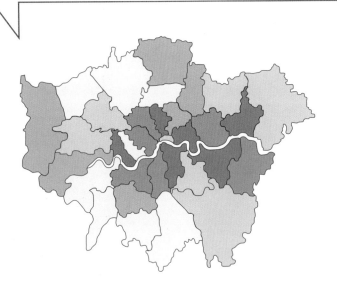

**Lung cancer death rates (1996)**

age standardised rate per 100,000

- ⬤ 60 to 84
- ⬤ 51 to 53
- ⬤ 48 to 50
- ⬤ 45 to 47
- ◯ 35 to 44

environment

health

## 3.1a Poor quality housing

Local authorities survey housing and assess its quality. Poor quality housing can lead to accidents, infections (eg inadequate kitchens) and fires (through poor electrical supply).

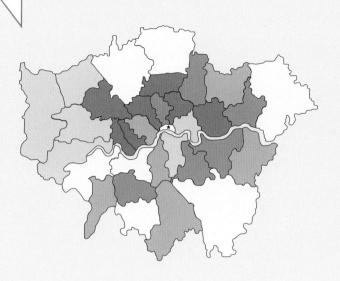

**Private sector houses in poor condition (1998)**

percent unfit houses

- 14.2 to 21.3
- 10.6 to 13.6
- 8.1 to 9.7
- 5.6 to 7.5
- 2.0 to 5.2
- ★ no data

3. Housing

## 3.1b Falls at home

Falls are a relatively common cause of injury, even death, in frail older people. Along with social support, some protection can be achieved through better housing standards and design.

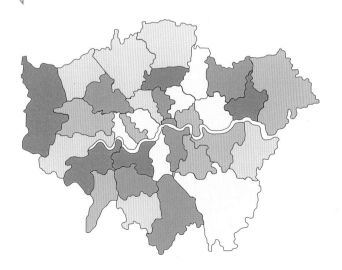

**Deaths from falls (1995-1997 annually)**

age standardised rate per 100,000

- 8.5 to 14.3
- 5.2 to 6.3
- 4.2 to 5.0
- 3.7 to 4.0
- 2.3 to 3.6

## 3.2a **Open spaces**

'Accessible open space' takes into account the distance an individual has to travel from their home to a public green space. Mental health can be supported by good town planning, with high quality housing and open spaces for a wide range of activities.

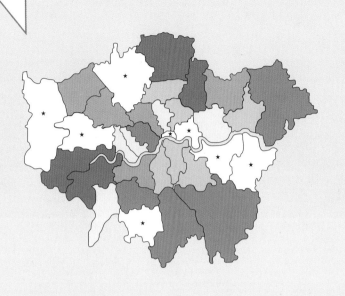

**Accessible open space (1994)**

square metres per person

- 54 to 116
- 32 to 38
- 21 to 25
- 18 to 19
- 2 to 12
- ★ no data

## 3.2b **Mental Health**

The causes of mental health are complex, arising from childhood experiences and life stresses. Admission to hospital for mental illness may be avoided with good community-based services. The variations between health authorities shown here reflect different service patterns as well as illness rates.

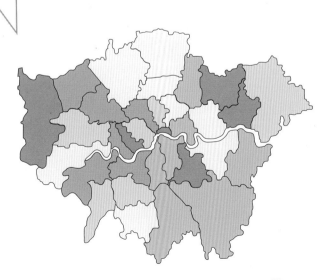

**Hospital episodes for neuroses, ages 15-74**

rate per 100,000

- 32 to 78
- 24 to 30
- 18 to 22
- 12 to 17
- 5 to 9

environment

health

## 3.3a Smoke detectors

More than half of all London homes have a smoke detector, but there are fewer in inner areas. A research study is currently assessing whether giving free alarms to households that do not have them can reduce deaths and injuries from fires.

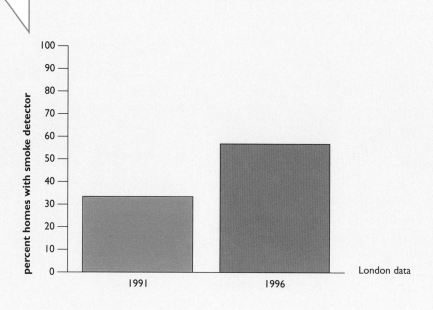

London data

## 3.3b Fires

There were over 8,000 fires involving the fire brigade in 1997, causing 82 deaths, 367 hospital admissions, 481 requiring a rescue and 318 injuries. Preventable causes of fires include kitchen equipment and smoking.

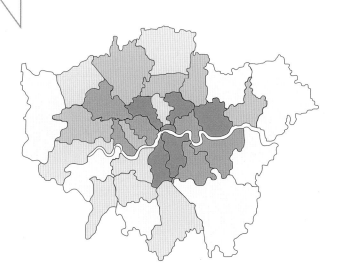

**House fires attended by London Fire Brigade (1997)**

rate per 100,000

- ◯ 160 to 288
- ◯ 135 to 154
- ◯ 93 to 118
- ◯ 83 to 92
- ◯ 39 to 80

## 3.4a Homeless

Approximately 25,000 people are accepted each year by London boroughs as officially homeless. Half are from ethnic minority groups. Shelter, a charity for homeless people, estimates that there are another 63,000 'hidden homeless' who do not appear in official statistics and may be sleeping rough or temporarily in other people's accommodation.

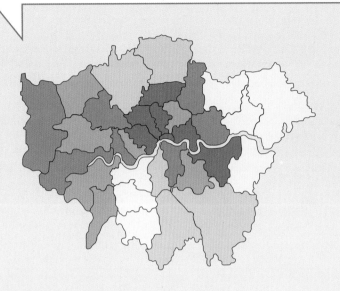

**People accepted by boroughs as homeless (1997)** 1998

**rate per 100,000 residents** rate per 1000
- 5.3 to 8.5
- 3.8 to 4.8
- 3.0 to 3.6
- 2.0 to 2.9
- 0.4 to 1.7

## 3.4b Tuberculosis

Tuberculosis is more common in homeless people, partly because the disease may recur with the exposure and poor nutrition that accompany homelessness. However, the majority of new TB notifications are in recent migrants from parts of the world where the disease remains common.

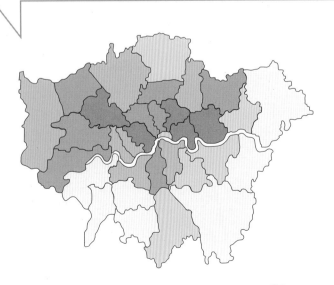

**Tuberculosis notifications (1996)**

**rate per 100,000 residents**
- 46 to 85
- 33 to 43
- 21 to 26
- 14 to 19
- 4 to 13

## 4.1a Journeys

Transport is a major problem in London. Cars predominate yet make roads dangerous for other pedestrians and cyclists, and create pollution. Public transport is the second commonest mode of travel. Underground and overland train services are not integrated, and are overcrowded for commuters. Buses are slowed by other traffic. Short journeys are expensive, and ordinary tickets do not allow transfer between different modes for a single journey.

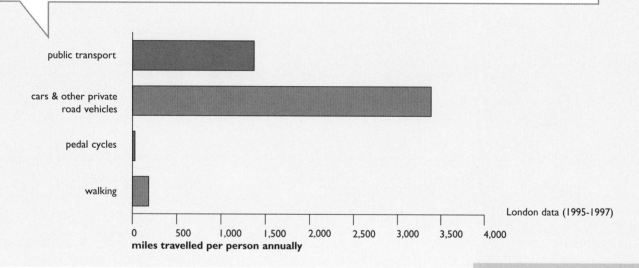

London data (1995-1997)

**miles travelled per person annually**

## 4.1b Road deaths and serious injuries

Over 200 people are killed on the roads in London each year, and more than 6,000 have serious injuries. The majority of people dying are pedestrians, while second most common are accidents between car drivers. Serious injuries are most frequently reported in car drivers.

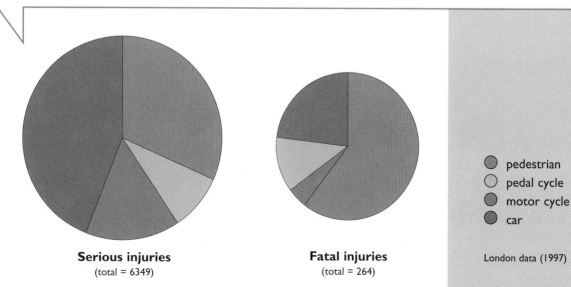

**Serious injuries**
(total = 6349)

**Fatal injuries**
(total = 264)

- pedestrian
- pedal cycle
- motor cycle
- car

London data (1997)

## 4.2a Reasons for journeys

Most personal journeys are for shopping, personal visits and leisure activities. One journey in five is related to work.

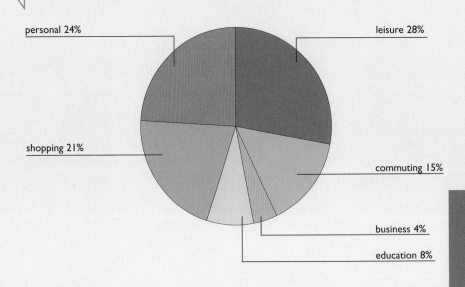

personal 24%

leisure 28%

shopping 21%

commuting 15%

business 4%

education 8%

**Journeys per person per year (1995-1997)**

London data

## 4.2b Casualties on London roads

There are higher rates of car ownership per household in outer than inner London, but high death and serious injury rates occur where there are greater car speeds (for example, the main 'arterial' road routes) and in inner London where there is more traffic and more pedestrians.

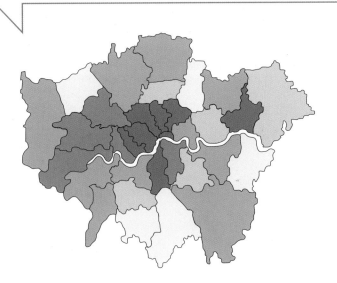

**Road casualties fatal and serious**

rate per 1,000 residents

- 12 to 116
- 11
- 10
- 9
- 6 to 8

## 4.3a Cycling

Fewer than two percent of London journeys are by cycle (compared, for example, with 25 percent in York). The number of cycling journeys by children of school age has fallen by 60 percent in the last decade.

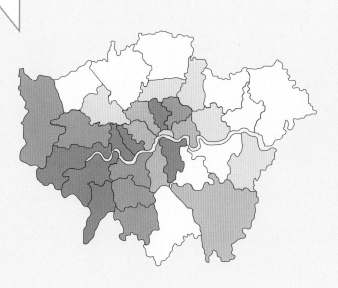

**Daily cycle trips**

rate per 1,000 residents (1991)

- 60 to 109
- 52 to 58
- 40 to 48
- 28 to 38
- 19 to 27

## 4.3b Heart disease

Heart disease is a major cause of death and disability. Physical exercise, not smoking, good diet and control of blood pressure protect from heart disease. Cycling and walking are important means of regular exercise, yet surveys in local boroughs have shown that up to 20 percent of Londoners take no physical exercise at all.

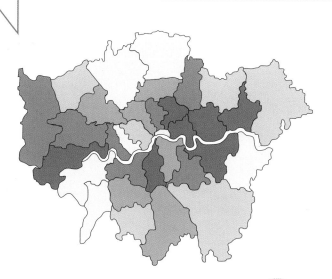

**Deaths from circulatory diseases, people under 65**

age standardised rate per 100,000

- 81 to 112
- 73 to 77
- 59 to 71
- 52 to 57
- 36 to 50

1995-7

Data slightly wrong!

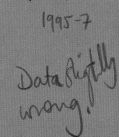

## 5.1a **Air pollution trends**

London's air is becoming less polluted with smoke and sulphur dioxide because of the change in domestic heating from coal to oil, gas and electricity, and through economic changes from manufacturing to service industries. Pollution from road transport, however, is rising. Diesel engines produce particles, cars produce greenhouse gases.

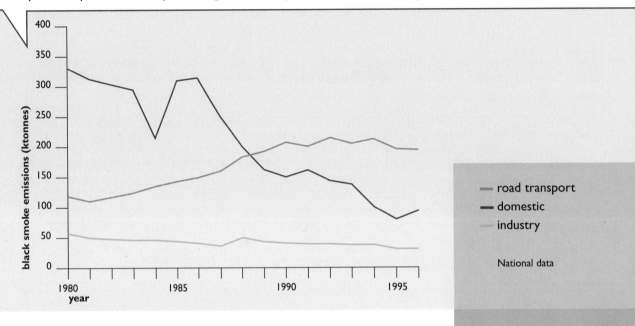

road transport
domestic
industry

National data

## 5.1b **Respiratory illness**

Hospital admissions for respiratory illness are more frequent in winter, often due to respiratory infections in people with chronic lung disease. Air pollution in summer can also increase admissions. Smoking is the commonest cause of chronic lung disease in adults.

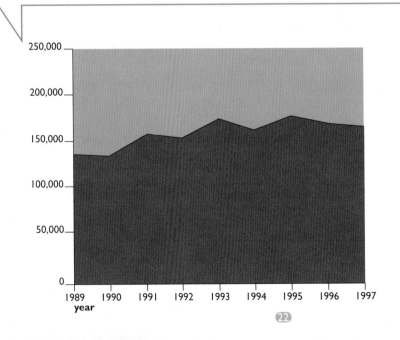

Hospital admissions for respitory illness

London data

## 5.2a Air pollution across London

Air quality is measured at sites across London. Local conditions (eg whether traffic is moving or static, and the weather) affect the measures. Nitrogen dioxide is a 'greenhouse' gas produced by motor engines that is contributing to global warming. Ozone, produced by sunlight acting on vehicle exhaust gases, can cause respiratory symptoms such as asthma. Particulates – soot and dust particles – also exacerbate lung disease.

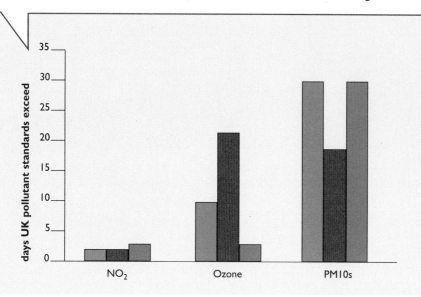

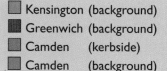

Kensington (background)
Greenwich (background)
Camden (kerbside)
Camden (background)

**(1997)**

**UK standards**

$NO_2$ = 150ppb

Ozone = 50ppb

PM10s = $50\mu/m^3$

## 5.2b Asthma

There is debate whether asthma is increasing. The two main causes of asthma are indoor air (from mites in house dust and mould) and pollens during the summer. Air pollution from cars has only a small effect on total asthma rates.

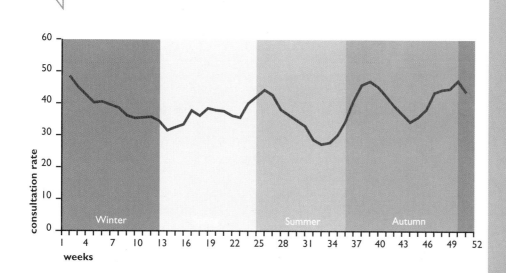

**Asthma consultations (1996)**

per week per 100,000

(3 week moving average)

National data

## 5.3a **Air quality along road networks**

Central London, Heathrow airport and the main roads carrying high volumes of traffic create London's geographical pattern of air pollution.

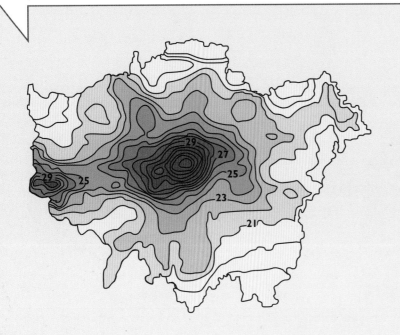

**Annual average nitrogen dioxide levels (1997)**

national air quality standard
= 21 parts per billion
Source: SEIPH

## 5.3b Hospital admissions for respiratory illness

Pneumonia can be fatal, especially in elderly people. Rates of hospital admission for respiratory illness do not show the same pattern as air pollution. Variations between boroughs may be due to differences in smoking, housing, or social circumstances.

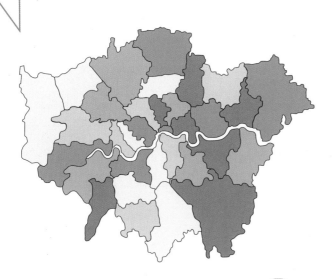

**Hospital admissions for respitory illness (1997)**
rate per 1,000

- 52 to 58
- 48 to 50
- 46 to 47
- 44 to 45
- 35 to 43

## 6.1a Drinking water quality

London's drinking water comes mainly from rivers, with some supply from deep wells. Measurements of water quality are made from domestic taps. Lead can be absorbed from pipes – some London homes are still connected through lead pipes. Chemical treatment can reduce lead absorption, but new European Commission standards will require replacing some pipes.

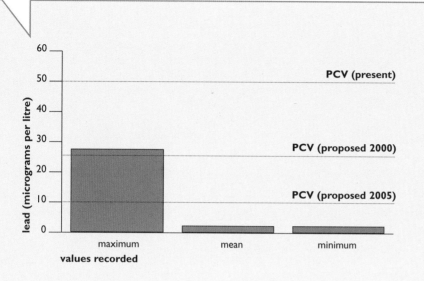

PCV = permitted control value

London data (1997/98)

6 Water

## 6.1b Educational performance

Lead can affect mental ability, especially during childhood. But lead is not routinely measured in children, and nor is mental ability. School performance is only an approximate measure of mental ability, as it is influenced both by home background and quality of schools.

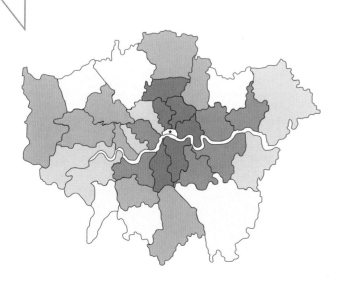

**Young people not gaining GCSE exam passes at grade A-C**

*1999*

percent

- 70 to 76
- 65 to 68
- 55 to 62
- 49 to 54
- 42 to 47
- ★ no data

## 6.2a Fluoride

London water has little natural fluoride. Fluoridation to levels that would prevent tooth decay has been proposed by London health authorities, but not agreed by the agencies responsible for water supply.

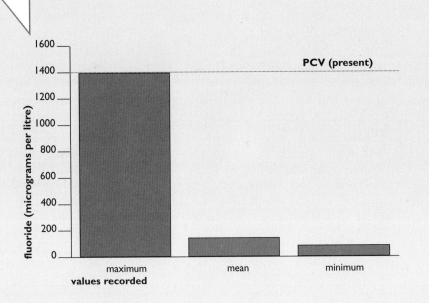

PCV (present)

fluoride (micrograms per litre)

maximum          mean          minimum

**values recorded**

PCV = permitted control value

London data (1997/98)

## 6.2b Tooth decay

Fluoridation would help the minority of London children whose poor personal dental hygiene and diet create severe tooth decay.

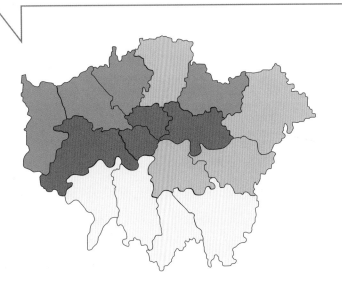

**5 year olds with tooth decay (1995/96)**

percent one or more teeth decayed, missing or filled

- 48.8 to 53.1
- 43.9 to 46.8
- 35.8 to 41.1
- 26.6 to 35.6

health districts

## 6.3a **Water pollution**

Water pollution may occur from industrial sources, seepage from sewage or from agricultural chemicals reaching natural water reservoirs. Bacterial and viral contamination of water is normally well controlled through chlorination and other cleansing treatments.

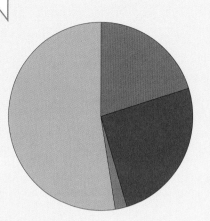

**all pollution incidents**
(total =1959)

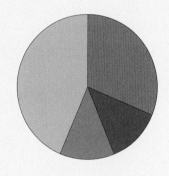

**major incidents**
(total =18)

 industrial

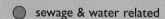 sewage & water related

 agricultural

 other

London data (1996)

## 6.3b **Water-borne infections**

Cryptosporidium infection mainly occurs through water supply, although some people are infected from other sources such as food.

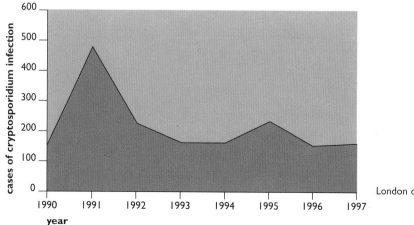

London data

## 7.1a Noise perception

It is not known whether constant exposure to low levels of noise, such as from traffic, may cause deafness. Industrial exposure over long periods can cause deafness.

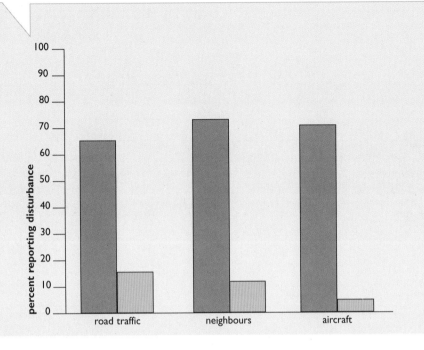

disturbed by noise at times

noise affects sleep or rest

National data (1991)

## 7.1b Deafness

Deafness is more common in older age, usually through degeneration of the hearing mechanisms within the ear. Borough rates may vary because local services have different criteria for registration, and probably underestimate the true extent of deafness.

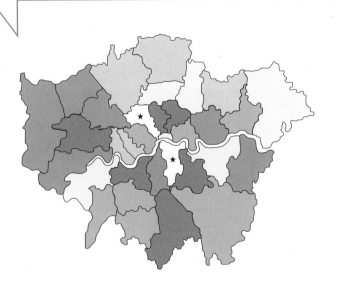

**People aged 18-64 registered as deaf (1998)**

rate per 100,000 residents

- 188 to 239
- 140 to 176
- 114 to 137
- 84 to 107
- 25 to 75
- ★ no data

## 7.2a **Noise complaints**

Data on noise exposures at borough level comes from individual complaints made by the public. The commonest reason is 'domestic' noise – noisy neighbours – and complaints are rising.

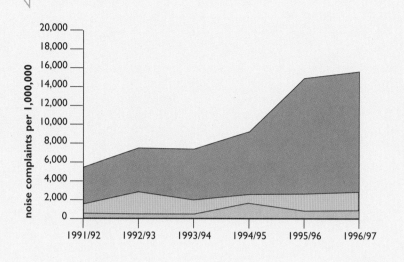

- ● domestic
- ○ industrial & commercial
- ○ construction sites etc.

London data

## 7.2b **Sleep disturbance**

Studies around London Heathrow Airport indicate that aircraft noise disturbs the sleep of some local residents. A research study is investigating the psychological effects.

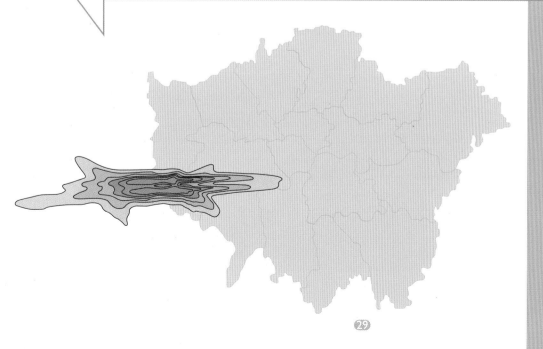

**Noise exposure**

- ● high exposure
  69+ Leq
- ○ medium exposure
  63-68 Leq
- ○ low exposure
  59-62 Leq

Leq = equivalent continuous
sound level

## 8.1a Waste disposal

Most of London's household waste is collected by refuse vehicles, and taken by boat to landfill sites in the Thames estuary. A small proportion is incinerated to produce power. Both landfill and incineration can produce toxic gases if not properly managed, and water pollution may also occur.

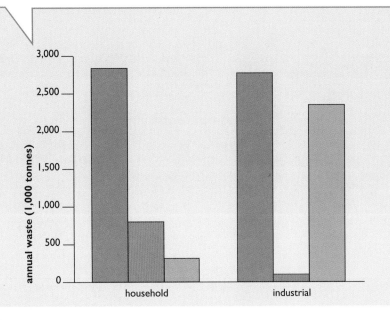

landfill
incineration
recycled

London data (1996)

## 8.1b Cancer

About one in four people develop cancer over their lifetime. Smoking is the most important single cause, while diet is probably also influential. Substances disposed of in refuse, for example metals from batteries such as cadmium, can produce cancer and birth defects. There is no evidence that current solid waste disposal is causing cancer.

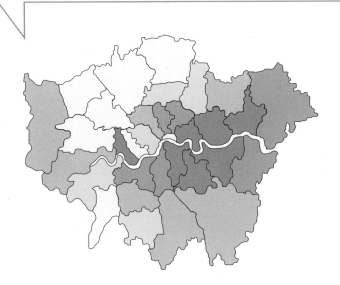

**Deaths from cancer**

**rate per 100,000**

(annually 1995-1997)

○ 215 to 240
○ 197 to 208
○ 193 to 195
○ 185 to 190
○ 164 to 184

## 8.2a Household waste collection

At present only a tenth of London's domestic waste (by weight) is recycled, and one fifth is deposited at amenity sites. Most industrial waste, by weight, comes from building demolition and construction, and is considered non-toxic. Special waste (including medical waste) can contain poisonous materials, and is treated separately – often incinerated rather than placed in land-fill.

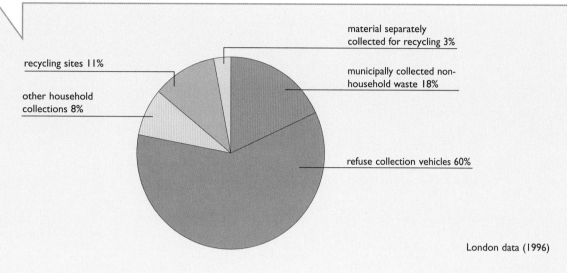

material separately collected for recycling 3%

municipally collected non-household waste 18%

recycling sites 11%

other household collections 8%

refuse collection vehicles 60%

London data (1996)

## 8.2b Birth defects

The causes of birth defects are not well understood, but include spontaneous genetic changes and environmental influences from diet. Some materials within waste would be directly dangerous if they were to enter food or water supplies.

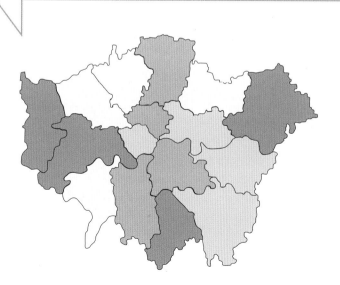

**Down's syndrome, anencephalus, spina bifida (1995-1997)**

rate per 10,000 births

◯ 8.1 to 17.4
◯ 5.1 to 7.9
◯ 3.1 to 4.0
◯ 0.8 to 2.4

health districts

## 9.1a Medical sources

Natural radiation from the earth is low in London. Man-made causes include radiation used in hospitals for investigation (eg x-rays) and cancer treatment (radiotherapy). There is strict control of exposure for both patients and staff.

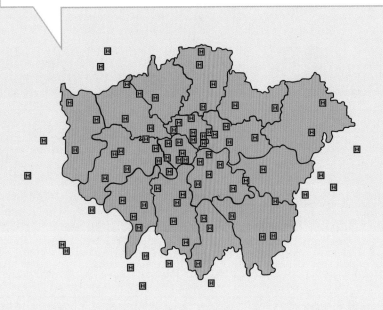

H hospitals with radiology departments

## 9.1b Leukaemia

The causes of laeukemia are largely unknown. Background cosmic radiation is one factor. Medical sources, for example x-rays in pregnancy, can potentially cause leukaemia.

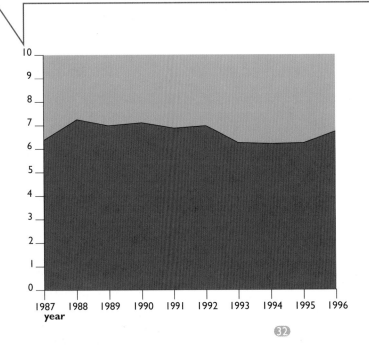

● Leukaemia incidence

age standardised rate per 100,000

London data

Trains carrying nuclear waste every week through London to Sellafield in the north of England for reprocessing. The World Health Organisation has recommended that "steps should be taken to provide for public participation in the process of authorising transportation of nuclear and hazardous wastes, an activity with obvious health implications".

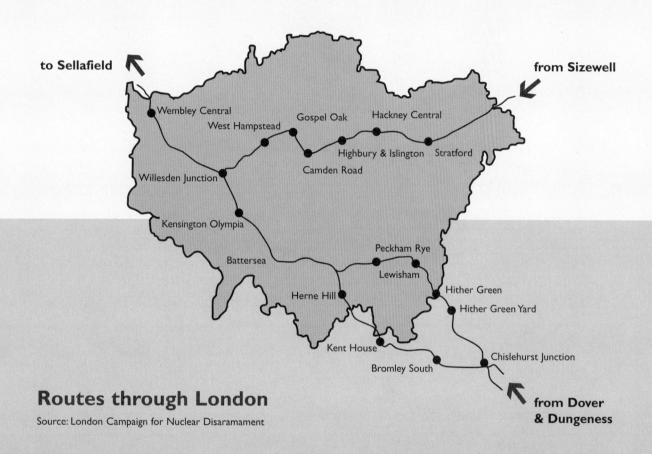

**Routes through London**

Source: London Campaign for Nuclear Disaramament

## 10.1a Energy use by sector

London has falling energy use by industry but increasing commercial and domestic use, especially for transport. London's energy is currently from non-renewable sources (oil, gas, coal), but in the future may draw from France where 30 percent is produced through nuclear power.

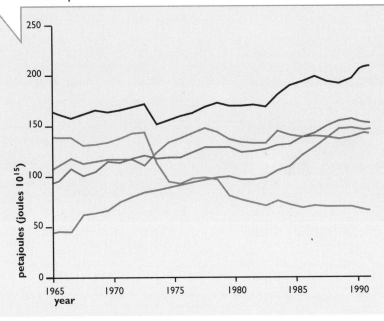

petajoules (joules $10^{15}$)

year

— domestic
— motor vehicles
— other transport
— commerce
— industry

London data

## 10.1b Excess winter deaths

Deaths in elderly people are more frequent in winter than summer months. There are several reasons, including more respiratory infections, fractures, and hypothermia. It is of interest, however, that some countries with very cold winter periods (eg Finland) do not have more deaths in winter, suggesting that Londoners may take inadequate precautions to protect themselves.

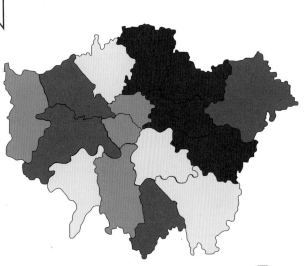

**Excess winter deaths in elderly people**

age 75+ rate per 100,000
(annually 1993-1995)

● 975 to 1060
● 860 to 929
● 782 to 850
○ 448 to 681

health districts

## consumption

| | | |
|---|---|---|
| water | 1,000 | million tonnes |
| oxygen | 40 | million tonnes |
| fuel | 20 | million tonnes |
| materials | 14 | million tonnes |
| food | 2 | million tonnes |

**10.2a**
## London's ecological 'footprint'

London consumes about 40 million tonnes of raw materials (excluding water and oxygen) each year and disposes of 22 million tonnes of industrial waste, household rubbish and sewage. Britain's surface area is about 24 million hectares – not far greater than London's 'ecological footprint'.

Source: Herbert Girardet

## waste

| | | |
|---|---|---|
| CO$_2$ | 60 | million tonnes |
| **industrial** | | |
| solids | 11 | million tonnes |
| liquids | 7 | million tonnes |
| **household** | | |
| refuse | 4 | million tonnes |

**surface area of London**     **0.15 million hectares**

**area required for:**

| | |
|---|---|
| carbon sequestration | 10.5 million hectares |
| food production | 8.4 million hectares |
| timber | 0.8 million hectares |

**total ecological footprint**     **19.7 million hectares**

## 10.2b Responsibilities

In 2000 a new Greater London Authority will take responsibility for strategic economic development, transport and environmental management for London. Some of these powers are at present held by the Government Office for London, which integrates regional policies of central government departments. However, the 33 local authorities will continue to provide housing, education, social services, and local environment regulation and planning.

The Department of Health has a Regional Office for London that coordinates 16 district health authorities, which in turn coordinate local hospital and community services. Many other public and private organisational bodies also have powers within London that contribute to London's environment and health, including the Health and Safety Executive (for workplace health), the Environment Agency, the emergency services (police, fire and ambulance), the privatised utilities (water, energy, some refuse disposal) and private employers.

Our report shows the need for continuing review and action across a wide range of environment and health issues in London. It is important that London's environment strategy is based on good health advice, and that the impacts of the environment on the population's health are properly assessed and measured.

photograph: Nigel Young

Model view of the new headquarters for the Greater London Authority.

# Review of the data

| | Association of environmental measures with diseases<br><br>weak ☆<br>medium ☆☆<br>strong ☆☆☆ | Trend of environment and health indicators<br><br>deteriorating ☆<br>level ☆☆<br>improving ☆☆☆ | Data availability<br><br>poor ☆<br>medium ☆☆<br>good ☆☆☆ |
|---|---|---|---|
| Quality of life | ☆☆ | ☆☆ | ☆☆☆ |
| Food, alcohol, tobacco | ☆☆☆ | ☆☆ | ☆☆ |
| Housing | ☆ | ☆☆ | ☆ |
| Transport | ☆☆ | ☆ | ☆☆ |
| Air | ☆ | ☆☆ | ☆☆☆ |
| Water | ☆☆ | ☆☆ | ☆☆ |
| Noise | ☆ | ☆☆ | ☆ |
| Refuse | ☆ | ☆☆ | ☆ |
| Radiation | ☆ | ☆☆ | ☆ |
| Sustainability | ☆☆ | ☆ | ☆☆ |

# References & further reading

## 1    Quality of life

1.1a    Burrows R and Rhodes D. *Unpopular places? Area disadvantage and the geography of misery in England.* Policy Press, Centre for Housing Policy, University of York, 1998. http://www.york.ac.uk/inst/chp/misery.htm

1.1b    Evening Standard. *London a city on the sick list.* 10 December 1998, (MORI poll for King's Fund)

1.2a    Population and Health Monitor PP1 98/1. Office for National Statistics, 1998.

1.2b    *Morbidity Statistics from General Practice 1991-92.* Office for National Statistics, 1998.

1.3a    Public Health Common Data Set 1998.

1.3b    Public Health Common Data Set 1998.

1.4a    *Control of Immigration: statistics United Kingdom, first half 1998.* Home Office Statistical Bulletin 24/98.

1.4b    Population and Health Monitor PP1 98/1. Office for National Statistics, 1998.

1.5a    *Annual Employment Survey 1997.* Office for National Statistics, 1997.

1.5b    *Labour Market Trends April 1999.* Office for National Statistics, 1999.

•    *London at work.* London Research Centre, 1998.

•    *The Capital Divided: Mapping Poverty and Social Exclusion in London.* London Research Centre, 1996.

•    Benzeval M, Judge K and Soloman M. *The health status of Londoners: a comparative perspective.* King's Fund Institute, 1992.

## 2    Food, alcohol, tobacco

2.1a    Official Control of Foodstuffs Form A Inspection Statistics. Ministry of Agriculture, Fisheries and Food (unpublished).

2.1b    Public Health Laboratory Service Communicable Disease Surveillance Centre (unpublished). http://www.phls.co.uk/facts/index.htm

2.2a    *Regional Trends 33: 1998 edition.* Office for National Statistics. The Stationery Office, 1998. [more detailed information available from] *National Food Survey 1997: annual report on food expenditure, consumption and nutrient intakes.* Ministry of Agriculture, Fisheries and Food, 1999. http://www.maff.gov.uk/esg/pubs/pubs.htm

2.2b    Prescott-Clarke P and Primatesta P. *Health Survey for England 1996 Volume 1.* The Stationery Office, 1998.

2.3a    *Liquor Licensing, England and Wales, July 1997-June 1998.* Statistical Bulletin 27/98. Home Office, 1998.

2.3b    Public Health Common Data Set 1998.

2.4a    *Living in Britain: results from the General Household Survey.* Office for National Statistics. The Stationery Office, 1998.

2.4b    *Trends in Our Healthier Nation mortality targets: London Boroughs 1979-1996.* Health of Londoner's Project, 1997.

## 3    Housing

3.1a    London Borough HIP Submissions, 1996.

3.1b    Public Health Common Data Set 1998.

3.2a    *State of the Environment Report for 1996.* London Planning Advisory Committee, 1997.

3.2b    Public Health Common Data Set 1998.

3.3a    *English House Condition Survey 1996.* Department of Environment, Transport and the Regions. The Stationery Office, 1998.

3.3b    London Fire Brigade, 1997 (unpublished).

3.4a    London Borough HIP Submissions.

3.4b    Public Health Laboratory Service, Communicable Disease Surveillance Centre (unpublished).

•    *The real cost of poor homes: a critical review of the literature.* University of Westminster and University of Sussex (1996), Royal Institution of Chartered Surveyors. http://www.rics.org.uk/research/output.html

•    Johnson S et al. *London's Mental Health.* Kings Fund, 1997.

•    Roberts I. *Smoke alarm use: national prevalence and household predictors.* Injury Prevention 1996;2:263-265.

•    Ramsden S, Bau S and El Kabir D J. *Tuberculosis among the central London single homeless: a four year retrospective study.* Journal of the Royal College of Physicians 1988;22:16-7.

## 4    Transport

4.1a    *National Travel Survey 1995-97.* Department of the Environment, Transport and the Regions, 1999 (unpublished).

4.1b    London Research Centre (unpublished).

4.2a    *National Travel Survey 1995-97.* Department of the Environment, Transport and the Regions, 1999 (unpublished).

4.2b    London Research Centre (unpublished).

4.3a    *Travel in London: London Area Transport Survey 1991.* London Research Centre (unpublished).

4.3b    Public Health Common Data Set 1998.

•    *Reducing road traffic in London – proposed strategy.* London Planning Advisory Committee, 1999.

•    Söderlund N, Ferguson J and McCarthy M. *Transport in London and the implications for health.* The Health of Londoner's Project, 1996.

•    *A cycling strategy for London.* London Planning Advisory Committee, 1977. http://www.lpac.gov.uk/finalcyc.html

# 5 Air

5.1a National Environmental Technology Centre, 1999.
http://www.aeat.co.uk/netcen/airqual/welcome.html

5.1b Hospital Episode Statistics (ICD-9 codes 460-519). Department of Health (unpublished).

5.2a National Environmental Technology Centre, 1999.
http://www.aeat.co.uk/netcen/airqual/welcome.html.

5.2b Fleming D, Crombie D and Ross A. *Weekly Returns Service Report [annual report] for 1996.* Birmingham Research Unit, Royal College of General Practitioners, 1997.

5.3a South East Institute of Public Health, 1999.
http://www.seiph.umds.ac.uk/envhealth

5.3b Hospital Episode Statistics (ICD-9 codes 460-519). Department of Health (unpublished).

• *The Quantification of the Effects of Air Pollution on Health in the United Kingdom.* Committee on the Medical Aspects of Air Pollutants, Department of Health, 1997.

• *London Air Quality Review briefing report 1997.* South East Institute of Public Health.

# 6 Water

6.1a *London Wide Drinking Water Survey, 1997-8.* Severn Trent Laboratories Ltd. (Permitted control values: present, Water Supply Regulations and EEC Directive 80/778/EEC. Proposed levels, EC Directive 98/83/EC not yet in legislation in UK).

6.1b Department of Education and Employment, 1999 (unpublished).

6.2a *London Wide Drinking Water Survey, 1997-8.* Severn Trent Laboratories Ltd. (Permitted control values: present, Water Supply Regulations and EEC Directive 80/778/EEC).

6.2b The Health of Londoners Project, 1998 (unpublished).

6.3a *Water pollution incidence in England & Wales, 1996.* Environment Agency. Department of the Environment, Transport and the Regions. The Stationery Office: 1997.

6.3b Public Health Laboratory Service, Communicable Disease Surveillance Centre (unpublished).

• *Cryptosporidium in water supplies.* Drinking Water Inspectorate, Department of the Environment, Transport and the Regions, 1998.
http://www.dwi.detr.gov.uk/crypto/bou0.htm

# 7 Noise

7.1a *Effects of Environmental Noise on People at Home.* Building Research Establishment Information Paper 22/93. Construction Research Communications Ltd, 1993.

7.1b Department of Health, 1999 (unpublished).

7.2a *Environmental Health Report [annual report] 1996-7.* Chartered Institute of Environmental Health, 1999 (London data unpublished).

7.2b *RND reports 9902, 9903 & 9904, 1997.* Prepared by Directorate of Operational Research and Development on behalf of Department of Environment, Transport and the Regions.

• *Effects of environmental noise on people at home:* BRE information paper 22/93. Building Research Establishment, Construction Research Communications Ltd. http://www.bre.co.uk

• *National Noise Attitude Survey 1991,* Building Research Establishment.

# 8 Refuse

8.1a Municipal Waste Management 1995/6, Department of the Environment, Transport and the Regions.

8.1b Public Health Common Data Set 1998.

8.2a South East of England Waste Management Report on the 1996 survey. Environment Agency, 1998.

8.2b Public Health Common Data Set 1998.

• *Re-inventing waste: towards a London Waste Strategy.* London Planning Advisory Committee, 1997. http://www.lpac.gov.uk

• *Cancer in South East England 1996.* Thames Cancer Registry, 1997.

# 9   Radiation

9.1a   Camden & Islington Health Authority Information Team 1998.

9.1b   Cases of Leukaemia diagnosed between 1987 and 1996. Thames
Cancer Registry (unpublished).

9.2a   *Nuclear trains across London: an accident waiting to happen.* London
Campaign for Nuclear Disarmament, 1998.   [Source of quote] WHO
Pre-conference document EUR/ICP/EHCO/02 03 04/12: para 52


# 10 Sustainability

10.1a   *London Energy Study 1991.* London Research Centre, 1993.

10.1b   *Housing and health.* The Health of Londoners Project, 1998.

10.2a   Girardet H.   *Creating sustainable cities.*   Schumacher Society, 1999.

- *The London Study: a strategic framework for London,* Association of
London Government.
- *Health and Environment in Sustainable Development: five years after
the Earth Summit.* World Health Organisation, Geneva 1997.
- *Agendas for Change.* Chartered Institute of Environmental Health, 1997.